A Practical Guide to Staying on Track

EVERYDAY *Plant-Based* MEALS *You'll Just* LOVE

ZELDA JANE CURRY

Disclaimer: The author is not a medical doctor, and suggestions in this book are not medical advice. People with ailments, allergies or conditions that prohibit practices recommended in this book and people taking medication should consider dietary changes carefully and under the supervision of a medical doctor. The author is not responsible for adverse effects.

EVERYDAY PLANT-BASED MEALS YOU'LL JUST LOVE:
A PRACTICAL GUIDE TO STAYING ON TRACK

For permissions contact: zeldajayeveryday@gmail.com

Cover by Janet Levrel

ISBN: 978-1-7359113-1-1

First Edition: October 2020

Table of Contents

Introduction

No matter where you are in your plant-based journey, I hope this book will inspire your creativity. Whether you have a solid system for staying on track, or if you're only considering giving up meat and dairy, I welcome the chance to share with you what I've learned. I hope you'll want to put some of these things into practice.

I won't lie...

My own switch to a plant-based diet took some getting used to. If you've decided that you want to switch, too, and you're looking for support, just be patient with yourself and give it time. It's normal for a person's tastes to change. If you give dietary changes some time, you'll find it easier and more enjoyable to stay on track than it was at first.

At first, I missed all the foods I used to love, and when I started eating more beans and vegetables it took months for my system to adjust. It's been nearly five years, and now I'm one of those people who I used to make fun of. I enjoy the foods I eat VERY much, especially because my choices are highly intentional. I know my diet is making me healthier and healthier day by day, plate by plate.

The method described in this book is not always easy, but it is practical. Many people have a hard time staying on track with a plant-based diet. Prior planning and the constructive actions described in the following pages make it so much easier to stick with it. There are some recipes included, but this book isn't really a cookbook or a recipe book; it is intended as a logistical guide with effective strategies. I have intentionally left out many topics that you may have reasonably expected to keep the page-count down. I encourage you to seek out online sources for worthwhile information that is not included such as:

- A lot of recipes
- Recipes for plant-based versions of favorite meat-based foods
- Nutritional information for each of the recommended foods
- Health benefits of each of the recommended foods
- Step-by-step cooking instructions for staple foods (for example, rice and other grains, lentils, and beans)
- Basic food preparation instructions
- Best ways to store fruits and vegetables, to keep them fresh longer
- Alternatives for other types of restricted diets (for example, raw, low-carb, or gluten free).

Please see the Reference section to find great online sources where this type of information is made available by the experts.

I wasn't going to say this, but...

As I envisioned my practical guide, I had planned to steer clear of controversial topics. Generally speaking, I believe in the rights of individuals to make their own choices. It's not up to me to persuade anyone to switch to a plant-based diet. Besides, how can we know for sure that new evidence won't come out showing that another way of eating is optimal? I'm not a medical doctor, nor a nutritionist. Nevertheless, as one curious and evolving human to another, I encourage each person to investigate the merits of a plant-based diet.

There are many reasons to change, so for those inclined, pick a reason, set your intention, and commit fully. Once you decide why eating a plant-based diet is important to you, rely on your "why" power,[1] not your "will" power, to make it real, and make it last.

---

[1] I would like to credit the source of "why" power vs. "will" power, but I'm not sure where it originated. I've heard it and read it many times from many sources.

Plant-based, Vegan, or Vegetarian? What's the Difference?

The focus of this book is maintaining a plant-based regimen for health reasons. A plant-based diet, also commonly referred to as a whole food plant-based (WFPB) diet, generally means a diet rich in fresh vegetables and fruits plus grains, legumes, nuts and seeds, and no animal products at all—no meat, poultry, seafood, dairy or eggs. A plant-based diet also has no derivatives of animal-based foods. WFPB also means that processed foods are avoided in favor of vegetables and fruits in their fresh, natural state.

The term "vegan" similarly implies the dietary restriction of animal-based foods and their derivatives, and it can include aspects of animal rights ideology, such as not wearing leather or fur for ethical reasons. Generally, the term "vegetarian" refers to diets that include dairy and eggs but exclude meat, poultry and seafood.

Why More People Are Switching to Plant-Based Diets

Especially in recent years, more and more people are "going vegan." Many people who have switched tout plant-based diets as highly beneficial in achieving better health. Like many people, I lost 30 pounds and kept it off after switching to a plant-based diet, reducing my risk for chronic illnesses. Many people see nagging ailments improve or go away completely. In the documentaries "Forks Over Knives" and "What the Health," people even successfully reversed chronic illnesses. Benefits and challenges can vary from person to person, so I offer no promises or guarantees. The documentary "The Game Changers" generated even more interest by touting the success of elite athletes on plant-based diets. There are many books, documentaries, podcasts, and YouTube videos that are drawing worldwide attention to the benefits of living plant-based.

Questions/Responses I Hear Most Often

When people ask how I've lost weight, or how I stay so fit and young-looking, and I tell them I switched to a plant-based diet, here are the responses I hear most often.

"I Could Never Do That, or I Could Never Give Up (fill-in-the-blank)"

I've heard a lot of people say they would like to try a plant-based diet, but they could never give up cheese, burgers, ice-cream, bacon, pepperoni pizza, you name it! But I believe that human beings can do just about anything they want to if they make it a priority. When people say, "Oh, I could never do that," the translation is, "I choose not to because it's not an important priority to me." That's okay; a plant-based diet isn't for everyone. I was no different. I ate animal products all my life before switching to a plant-based diet just five years ago.

When I first saw the documentary, “Forks Over Knives,” four years before I made the switch to a plant-based diet, I was very inspired. I could see that it made sense, but I just wasn't ready to give up dairy and eggs. Then, a cancer scare caused me to reevaluate my priorities, and since then I’ve followed a plant-based diet.

If you've decided that you want to make a change, or at least to try, I encourage you to find a way to make it work. The method I've proposed in this book may not be the way that works best for you; that's okay, too. I hope at the very least you'll find some encouragement and helpful tips in this book. It's worth it to change. There's a lot of satisfaction in knowing that the most fundamental choices you're making each day are consistent with your values and your long-term ability to thrive and contribute to the lives of those you care about.

“Where Do You Get Your Protein?”

Another response I hear a lot is, "Where do you get your protein if you don’t eat meat, poultry, fish, eggs or dairy?" The simple answer is I get protein from beans and leafy green vegetables, but there are deeper underlying problems with the premise of the question. Number one, we've been deceived by the food and exercise industry into thinking that we need more protein than we actually do; and number two, many people wrongly believe that protein that comes from animal sources is superior to or more complete than plant-based protein.

Most of us have never known of anyone suffering from a protein deficiency, yet almost everybody knows people who have diseases that are directly related to consuming animal products. A plant-based diet that includes normal amounts of beans, lentils, leafy greens, other vegetables and grains has all the protein a healthy human body requires. Note: Fruit doesn't have as much protein as beans, vegetables or grains. If a person ate nothing but fruit, they probably would not get enough protein.

"Where Do You Get Your Calcium?"

Another similar question is "Where do you get your calcium if you don't eat dairy?" Again, the simple answer is beans and leafy green vegetables, but again, there's more to the premise of this question. Advertising campaigns have told us for years that milk is an essential part of a balanced diet because it provides the calcium we need. I've come to understand that there are many health risks associated with eating dairy products, and there is no proven calcium-related advantage. Skeptical? Don't take my word for it. Check reputable sources such as nutritionfacts.org.

"What Do You Eat for Breakfast?"

This question comes up a lot, or people often ask what someone on a plant-based diet eats in a day. The underlying premise of this question could be that the person asking is interested in trying a plant-based diet, but wonders how to even begin. It's true, switching to a plant-based diet takes some re-conditioning. Certain information and cooking techniques can be very helpful. This book gives suggestions for breakfast and other meals, based on a practical meal planning method.

What to Eat on a Plant-Based Diet:

Basic Principles for Creating Delicious, Nutritious, Health-Promoting Plates

Just because a food contains no animal products does not necessarily mean it is health-promoting. For example, some well-known brands of commercially-produced candy, cookies and chips are known to be "vegan" based on their meat-and-dairy-free list of ingredients, yet those foods bear no resemblance at all to the foods recommended in this book. The focus is to eat a health-promoting diet that incorporates a high volume of health-promoting foods. In the next several sections, based on information and principles I've learned, I will describe a method to incorporate the advice of plant-based experts day by day.

Foods to Eat

Fresh, whole, or minimally-processed, organic, non-GMO plant-based foods. The most desirable food options have the following qualities:

- Nutritionally-dense
- Low in fat
- High in fiber
- Overall calorie density suited to maintaining healthy body mass index

Foods to Eliminate

- Animal products including meat, poultry, seafood, dairy products and eggs
- Processed foods with ingredients made from animal products (read labels carefully)

Foods to Limit or Avoid

- Highly processed grains (flour and foods made from flour)
- Processed sugars (and foods made with processed sugars)
- Fried foods
- Oil
- Salt
- Sweeteners

Other Guidelines

- Choose whole, fresh vegetables and fruits, mostly raw
- Cooked vegetables are okay too, using the following methods:
  - Steam: On the stove or in the microwave
  - Sauté: In a pan on the stove without oil, using water or vegetable broth
  - Boil: On the stove
  - Bake: In the oven or microwave
  - Roast: In the oven

Prioritizing Foods to Eat: Guidelines from the Experts

PCRM's Power Plate

When I took *Food for Life* nutrition classes at the Physicians Committee for Responsible Medicine (PCRM, an organization led by the well-known physician and author Dr. Neal Barnard), I learned about the Power Plate, which re-defines the four food groups as vegetables, fruits, legumes, and grains; entirely plant-based. Nuts and seeds are okay too, but in small amounts. The main points of PCRM's recommendations are to eat at least four servings of vegetables and three servings of fruit daily, minimize oils and fats, and eat foods rich in fiber.

Dr. Greger's "Daily Dozen"

In his well-known book about using a plant-based diet to avoid preventable illnesses, How Not to Die, Dr. Michael Greger's "Daily Dozen" checklist includes 10 plant-based foods to eat each day (Number 11 of the Daily Dozen is beverages and Number 12 is exercise). The food categories are beans, berries, other fruit (fruit other than berries), cruciferous vegetables, leafy greens, other vegetables (vegetables other than cruciferous and leafy greens), whole grains, flaxseeds, nuts, and spices.

Dr. Fuhrman's Nutritarian Food Pyramid and "G-BOMBS"

Dr. Joel Fuhrman's nutritarian food pyramid re-defines the conventional food pyramid with plant-based food groups arranged according to daily recommended percentages of calories. Dr. Fuhrman also recommends including "G-BOMBS" (a useful memory cue for health-promoting foods to eat each day). G-BOMBS stands for greens, beans, onions, mushrooms, berries, (nuts and) seeds.

Intro to Menu Palettes: Putting Expert Advice into Practice

The method described in this book can help you implement the guidelines suggested by experts, one plate, one day, one week at a time. As an alternative to recipes, the method of optimizing food choices by using "menu palettes" will provide more flexibility to make it easier to stay on track plate after plate, day after day, week after week.

Maintaining food checklists can be crazy-making when life gets in the way, even with an app. Menu palette options were inspired by the PCRM “Power Plate,” Dr. Greger's "Daily Dozen," and Dr. Fuhrman's "G-BOMBS." My hope is that menu palettes will serve as practical guidance, enabling you to incorporate tried-and-true nutritional advice in the time you have available.

Getting Started with Plant Based Meals: Menu Palettes

What is a Menu Palette?

A menu palette is an organized collection of food options from which you can create a variety of meals. Menu palettes are inspirational suggestions for structured improvisation. Using menu palettes is similar to an artist painting from a palette of colors or a jazz musician improvising from a lead sheet. The structure is there, but the rest is up to you. The advantage of menu palettes over recipes is that because you choose which ingredients to use, meals can be designed to suit your tastes exactly. You can substitute menu palette options freely based on what you like, what you're in the mood for, and what you have available.

For example, every day you can eat essentially the same breakfast, but change it by adding or excluding ingredients at will, so each time it can feel like a new experience. Or, if you prefer, you can make your favorite breakfast your favorite way every time; it's up to you. When you're short on time, you can eliminate the more time-consuming options to finish preparing the meal faster. Even if you run out of all but one or two menu palette options, it works fine, and you're on track.

The menu palettes provided in this book are not intended to be an exhaustive list of what to eat. Menu palettes are a supportive method to consistently achieve the nutritional targets in a routine manner. Menu palettes can be used for a large percentage of meals throughout the week, but feel free to eat other types of meals as well and use other types of recipes for more variety.

What You'll Need

The menu palette method works best for everyday meals that you prepare at home with groceries you've selected from the list of menu palette options. In addition to produce and grocery items, you'll also need kitchen supplies, but hopefully nothing that you don't already have. Common kitchen items including a cutting board, strainer, pots, pans, a toaster and a blender should be enough gear for all the menu palettes included in this book.

Ingredients

As much as possible, all ingredients should be fresh, minimally-processed, organic, non-GMO and have no added salt, oil or sugar. Dried spices and herbs are fine, but make sure they are organic with no added salt, oil or sugar. If it's not possible to get organic produce, then use conventional, avoiding the Environmental Working Group's "Dirty Dozen," an annual list of the most pesticide-prone crops. Instead, try to use produce listed on the EWG's "Clean 15" list, as they are considered to be safer. You can find these lists on the Environmental Working Group's website: www.ewg.org.

The listed menu palette options are suggestions that work well within the palette, but feel free to experiment. Choose options in a way that the flavors go well together, and are pleasing to you. There's no need to measure or limit most ingredients; it's fine to eat as much as you like of most fresh vegetables and fruits, assuming you have no allergies, health-related restrictions, and you don't eat way more than a normal person would. (Dr. Greger's "Daily Dozen" is great guidance on how much of each type of food to eat each day. See "Recommended Daily Servings: Dr. Greger's "Daily Dozen" on page 53 or nutritionfacts.org.)

If you prefer to restrict gluten or grains, menu palettes can be made gluten-free or grain-free by making substitutions.

Principles of Menu Palette Design

My priorities for designing the menu palettes were:

- Create a go-to meal that isn't hard to prepare
- Make it *DELICIOUS*, so the plant-based habit never feels like a chore
- Make the most of every opportunity: load every meal with Daily Dozen and G-BOMBS foods
- Keep menu options modular so it's easy to create variations by changing basic ingredients

Note: For simplicity, menu palette option categories do not always line up with Daily Dozen categories. For example, the menu palette category "Other Vegetable Options" may include cruciferous vegetables or leafy greens, and the menu palette's "Fresh Fruit Options" and "Dried Fruit Options" categories may include berries. As you customize your meals using menu palettes, please try to incorporate cruciferous vegetables and berries where possible, to achieve daily targets.

Menu Palettes – A Starter Kit

Here is your menu palette "starter kit" – basic collections of foods that can help you tick off your Daily Dozen week after week. The five menu palettes below can yield hundreds of variations. Sample recipes are provided for each one, along with ideas for easy variations using different menu palette options.

Menu Palette #1: Grains with Fruit, Nuts and Seeds

- *Sample Recipe: Steel Cut Oats with Banana, Dried Fruit, Walnuts and Flaxseeds*

Menu Palette #2: Toast with Toppings

- *Sample Recipe: Sprouted Whole Grain Toast with Almond Butter and Fresh Fruit*
  Sample Recipe: Pita with Hummus and Vegetables

Menu Palette #3: Smoothie with Greens

- *Sample Recipe: Green Citrus Smoothie with Kale and Flaxseeds*

Menu Palette #4: Entree-Sized Salad

- *Sample Recipe: Green Leaf Entree Salad – Arugula, Radicchio, Beets, Berries and Walnuts with Baked Red Potato*

Menu Palette #5: Bean Bowl with Vegetables and Grains

- *Sample Recipe: Garbanzo Beans with Tomatoes and Peppers with Brown Rice*

Each Sample Recipe includes the following information:

- Target Index: A calculated rating based on a scale of 1 to 10, where a perfect 10 would include a full day's servings from the PCRM Power Plate, Dr. Greger's "Daily Dozen," and Dr. Fuhrman's "G-BOMBS. It is intended as a notional guide for comparing the Sample Recipes in terms of nutritional robustness and achieving daily targets.

- Calories (approximate)
- Protein (in grams)
- Carbohydrates (in grams)
- Fat (in grams)
- Fiber (in grams)
- Prep Time (in minutes)
- Shortcuts (if any)

For ease-of-use, the sample recipes for each menu palette are for one large serving. You can scale them up as needed to serve more people or scale them down to make snack-size portions.

Menu Palette #1: Grains with Fruit, Nuts and Seeds
Sample Recipe: Steel Cut Oats with Banana, Dried Fruit, Walnuts & Flaxseeds

Menu Palette #1
Grains with Fruit, Nuts & Seeds

Does oatmeal for breakfast sound boring?
It doesn't have to be!

Grain Options
Oats
Buckwheat
Millet
Brown rice

Fresh Fruit Options
Apples
Bananas
Blackberries
Blueberries
Raspberries
Strawberries

Dried Fruit Options
Raisins
Dates
Tart Cherries
Cranberries
Apricots
Prunes
Apples
Figs
Papaya
Mango

Nut Options
Walnuts
Pecans
Almonds
Cashews
Peanuts

Seed Options
Flax (ground)
Chia
Sesame

Spice Options
Cinnamon
Nutmeg
Ginger
Clove
Vanilla extract
Almond extract

Sweetener Options
Maple syrup
Honey
Agave
Molasses

Other Options
Plant-based milk or creamer

Menu Palette #1: Grains with Fruit, Nuts and Seeds

Sample Recipe: Steel Cut Oats with Banana, Dried Fruit, Walnuts and Flaxseeds

Protein: 7.4 g
Carbohydrates: 66 g
Fat: 15.7 g
Fiber: 9.9 g

Target Index: 3.3
Calories: 515

Prep Time: 25 minutes; shortcut: use quick oats

Menu Palette Option	Amount (US)	Amount (Metric)
Grain option: Steel cut oats	1/2 cup cooked (about 1/4 cup dry)	21 g dry
Fresh fruit option: Banana	1 medium banana, sliced	1 medium banana, sliced
Dried fruit option: Raisins and Dates	1/4 cup combined	38 g
Nut option: Walnuts	1/4 cup, pieces	25 g, pieces
Seed option: Flaxseeds (ground)	1 Tablespoon	7 g
Spice option: Vanilla extract	1/4 teaspoon	1.2 mL
Spice option: Cinnamon	A big sprinkle	A big sprinkle
Spice option: Nutmeg	A tiny sprinkle	A tiny sprinkle

Preparation Tips:

- Cook the oats according to the directions on the package, or in any way that you prefer. Oats can be boiled on the stove, microwaved, or soaked overnight.
- For stovetop cooking, boil the water, then add a dash of salt (optional), then the oats.
- While the oats are still cooking, add the vanilla and spices. The spice amounts listed are just recommendations; add the amounts of spices to suit your own tastes. The taste of nutmeg can be overpowering, so use just a little (unless you like it stronger).
- After the oats are cooked, stir in the ground flaxseeds. The texture can get too gooey if the flaxseeds are added while cooking.
- Add the fruit and the nuts last.
- If you don't like the texture of oatmeal—if it's too gloppy, pasty or slimy, try preparing it a different way, or use a different type of oats. Some of the less-processed types of oats have a very nice grainy texture, especially if cooked with just enough water (but not too much).
- If possible, use organic, non-GMO vanilla extract with no added alcohol.
- To reduce the calorie count, try cutting back on the fruit, nut and seed options.
- Try to get used to not adding a sweetener option, or try to use just a tiny drizzle. Sweeteners in general make food less healthy.

- Many vegans eliminate honey from their diet for ethical reasons; up to you.
- You can achieve a higher Target Index by substituting a half-cup of berries for the dried fruit.

Variations: Ideas for other sample recipes based on this menu palette

Here are a few ideas, but be creative and try your own!

- Oatmeal, fresh blueberries, almonds, chia seeds and cinnamon
- Buckwheat, cooked apples, raisins, walnuts, flaxseeds and cinnamon
- Brown rice, diced dried apricots, almonds, sesame seeds, cinnamon and a drizzle of honey (optional)
- Oatmeal, dried tart cherries, pecans, ground flaxseeds, and cinnamon
- Instead of grains, try a baked sweet potato with dried fruit and nut options.

Menu Palette #2: Toast with Toppings – Sweet Version
Sample Recipe: Sprouted Wheat Toast with Fruit

Menu Palette #2
Toast with Toppings

Two new takes on the old PB&J—sweet or savory!

Bread Options
Sprouted whole grain bread, bagels or English muffins

Nut Butter Options
Almond
Peanut
Cashew

Nut Options
Walnuts
Almonds
Cashews
Pecans
Peanuts

Fresh Fruit Options
Apricots
Banana
Blackberries
Blueberries
Kiwi
Mango
Melon
Peaches
Persimmon
Pineapple
Pomegranate seeds
Strawberries

Dried Fruit Options
Dates
Apricots
Apples
Banana chips
Figs
Prunes

Sweetener Options
Fruit preserves
Honey
Molasses

Menu Palette #2: Toast with Toppings – Sweet Version

Sample Recipe: Sprouted Whole Grain Toast with Almond Butter and Fresh Fruit

Protein: 17.9 g
Carbohydrates: 101.2 g
Fat: 18.4 g
Fiber: 19.7 g

Target Index: 3.3
Calories: 578

Preparation time: 20 minutes; shortcut: use fewer fruits

Menu Palette Option	Amount (US)	Amount (Metric)
Bread option: Sprouted whole grain bread	1 slice, toasted	1 slice, toasted
Nut butter option: Almond butter	2 Tablespoons	30 g
Fresh fruit option: Banana	1/2 medium, sliced	1/2 medium, sliced
Fresh fruit option: Kiwi	1 kiwi fruit, sliced	1 kiwi fruit, sliced
Fresh fruit option: Strawberries	1/2 cup, sliced	83 g, sliced
Fresh fruit option: Blueberries	1/2 cup	74 g
Fresh fruit option: Blackberries	1/2 cup	72 g
Fresh fruit option: Apricot	1 apricot, sliced	1 apricot, sliced
Fresh fruit option: Peach	1 medium-sized peach, sliced	1 medium-sized peach, sliced

Preparation tips:

- Slice fruit in the most attractive way you can. Have fun, experiment!
- Spread the almond butter on the bread and top with fruit, or the fruit can be served on-the-side.
- For variety, try different types of nut butter such as peanut, almond, or cashew, or try seed butters such as sunflower, pumpkin or sesame. Or you can try substituting whole nuts or seeds of your choice on the side such as walnuts, brazil nuts, cashews, almonds, hazelnuts, pumpkin seeds, sunflower seeds—and more!
- Enjoy with a cup of tea or coffee

Variations on Menu Palette #2 – Toast with Toppings – Sweet Version

- Sprouted raisin bread with almond butter, banana and dates
- Sprouted multigrain bread with peanut butter and sliced kiwi fruit
- Sprouted whole wheat English Muffin and peanut butter, pineapple, and banana
- Whole wheat bagel with fresh persimmon, walnuts, a sprinkle of cinnamon and a drizzle of honey

More Variations on Menu Palette #2: Toast with Toppings - Savory Version

Bread Options
Whole grain bread
Pita bread
Baked pita chips
Whole grain bagel
Sesame bagel

Protein-rich Spread Options
Hummus
Other bean or lentil spread

Leafy Green Vegetable Options
Arugula
Kale
Spinach
Fresh Parsley

Other Vegetable Options
Cucumbers
Tomatoes
Onions
Olives
Capers
Peppers

Menu Palette #2: Toast with Toppings – Savory Version

Sample Recipe: Pita with Hummus and Fresh Vegetables

Protein: 9.2 g
Carbohydrates: 36.8 g
Fat: 8.1 g
Fiber: 5.1 g

Target Index: 2.2
Calories: 244

Preparation time: 10 minutes

Menu Palette Option	Amount (US)	Amount (Metric)
Bread option: Whole wheat pita bread	1 pita, sliced	1 pita, sliced
Protein-rich spread option: Hummus	2 Tablespoons	30 g
Leafy green vegetable option: Arugula	1/2 cup	11 g
Leafy green vegetable option: Fresh parsley	5 sprigs	5 sprigs
Other vegetable option: Cucumber	3/4 cup, sliced	95 g
Other vegetable option: Tomato	10 grape tomatoes, sliced	10 grape tomatoes, sliced
Other vegetable option: Olive	5 olives	5 olives
Other vegetable option: Red onion	A few slices as a garnish	A few slices as a garnish

Preparation Tips:

- Artistically arrange the sliced vegetables on a plate, add the hummus and serve with bread
- Bored with hummus? Try creating a bean or lentil spread using legumes other than garbanzo beans. Be creative!

Variations

- Corn or whole wheat tortillas with black beans and tomato salsa with cilantro, avocados and red onions
- Sesame bagel with hummus, tomatoes, red onions and capers

Menu Palette #2: Toast with Toppings – Savory Version
Sample Recipe: Pita with Hummus and Vegetables

Menu Palette #3: Smoothie with Greens
Sample Recipe: Green Citrus Smoothie with Kale and Flaxseeds

Menu Palette #3
Smoothie with Greens

The quickest way to eat a full-days' worth of leafy greens!

Leafy Green Vegetable Options
Kale
Spinach

Liquid Options
Orange juice
Apple juice
Cold purified water

Other Vegetable Options
Cucumber
Fresh parsley
Fresh mint
Microgreens

Fruit Options
Banana
Pineapple
Papaya
Green apple
Green pear
Kiwi
Lime

Spice Options
Ginger root
Turmeric root or
Powdered turmeric

Seed Options
Ground flaxseeds
Hemp hearts

Menu Palette #3: Smoothie with Greens

Sample Recipe: Green Citrus Smoothie with Kale and Flaxseeds

Protein: 8.5 g
Carbohydrates: 70.8 g
Fat: 5.3 g
Fiber: 12 g
Prep time: 20 minutes; shortcut: pre-cut the fruit

Target Index: 5.0
Calories: 351

Menu Palette Option	Amount (US)	Amount (Metric)
Leafy green vegetable option: Kale	2 cups	67 g
Liquid option: Orange juice	1-1/2 cups	125 mL
Other vegetable option: Fresh parsley	3 Tablespoons	6.3 g
Other vegetable option: Fresh mint	2 Tablespoons	4.2 g
Fruit option: Frozen banana	3/4 medium	3/4 medium
Fruit option: Frozen pineapple	3/4 cup	114 g
Fruit option: Lime	1/4-inch circular slice with skin	0.6 cm circular slice with skin
Spice option: Ginger root	1-inch piece, peeled	2.5 cm-inch piece, peeled
Spice option: Turmeric root	1/2-inch piece, peeled	1.3 cm-inch piece, peeled
Seed option: Ground flaxseeds	1 Tablespoon	15 mL

Preparation Tips:

- For best results, blend all ingredients in a high-powered blender.
- If your flaxseeds aren't already ground, add them to the blender first alone, and grind them into a fine powder.
- Slice the lime, ginger root and turmeric root and put in the blender. You can substitute 1/4 teaspoon (0.8 g) of ground turmeric for fresh turmeric root.
- Add the orange juice. If your flaxseeds are already ground, add them after the orange juice for better blending.
- Add the kale, parsley and mint.
- Add the frozen fruit; adding the frozen fruit after the leafy greens is better for blending.
- Optional: Add ice cubes made from purified water if the fruit isn't frozen.
- Blend until the leafy greens are completely blended.
- The color of this smoothie is beautifully appetizing, unless you add something red (like beet greens or strawberries), so be careful.

Variations:

Ideas for other menu palatte options to add to the green citrus smoothie recipe.

- Green pear
- Green apple
- Cucumber
- Papaya
- Avocado

Menu Palette #4: Entree-sized Salad. Sample Recipe: Green Leaf Entree Salad: Arugula, Radicchio, Beets, Blueberries Garbanzo Beans and Walnuts

Menu Palette #4
Entree-Sized Salad

Choose colorful, eye-catching vegetables for a glorious celebration-on-a-plate!

Leafy Green Vegetable Options
Kale
Arugula
Spinach
Lettuce

Leafy Red Vegetable Options
Red cabbage
Radicchio
Red kale

Bean or Lentil Options
Garbanzo beans
French lentils

Other Vegetable Options
Cucumber
Sprouts
Microgreens
Beets
Radish
Onions
Celery
Jicama
Mushrooms
Tomatoes
Cooked Brussels sprouts
Carrots

Nut Options
Walnuts
Pecans
Almonds

Fresh Fruit Options
Blueberries
Blackberries
Raspberries
Apples
Persimmon
Pomegranate seeds

Dried Fruit Options
Raisins
Cranberries
Tart cherries
Dates
Apricots

Spice Options
Pepper
Oregano
Parsley
Turmeric

Dressing Options
Lemon juice
Lime juice
Vinegar
Oil free salad dressing
Salad dressing with oil
Extras
Avocado
Olives

Side Dish Options
Baked potato
Rice
Quinoa
Buckwheat
Millet
Bread

Menu Palette #4: Entree-Sized Salad

Sample Recipe: Green Leaf Entree Salad – Arugula, Radicchio, Beets, Berries and Walnuts with Baked Red Potato

Protein: 26.4 g
Carbohydrates: 87.9 g
Fat: 21.6 g

Fiber: 26.1 g
Target Index: 5.8
Calories: 617

Preparation time: 30 minutes
Shortcut: pre-cut the ingredients or use fewer options

Menu Palette Option	Amount (US)	Amount (Metric)
Leafy green vegetable option: Baby Arugula	2-1/2 cups	50 g
Leafy red vegetable option: Radicchio	1 cup, torn into small pieces	40 g, torn into small pieces
Bean or Lentil option: Garbanzo beans	1 cup, cooked	170 g, cooked
Other vegetable option: Cucumber	1 cup, sliced	120 g, sliced
Other vegetable option: Beets	3/4 cup, sliced	100 g, sliced
Other vegetable option: Watermelon radish	1/4 cup, sliced	50 g, sliced
Other vegetable option: Red onions	1/8 cup, sliced	6.5 g, sliced
Nut option: Walnuts	1/4 cup, pieces	25 g, pieces
Fresh fruit option: Blueberries	1/2 cup	74 g

Menu Palette Option	Amount (US)	Amount (Metric)
Spice option: Black pepper	A sprinkle, to taste	A sprinkle, to taste
Side dish option: Baked red potato	1 small	1 small

Preparation Tips:

- Wash and slice the produce, combine in a large bowl with the walnuts and garbanzo beans. Toss with dressing and serve.
- Take care in slicing vegetables in the most attractive way. It's generally faster to just use a simple knife, especially for one salad, but use a food processor or other equipment for more variety, if you have the time.
- Feel free to load up on leafy greens, no need to measure or limit them. It's okay to eat a HUGE salad if it's mostly leafy greens.
- Try this recipe with either blackberries or blueberries.
- Try to get used to eating salad without an oil-based salad dressing. Many commercially-produced salad dressings have unhealthy additives like salt, oil, sugar and preservatives; some may even have dairy or egg derivatives. If you want to skip the dressing, you can still dress your salad with zero-calorie options like lime juice, lemon juice or vinegar. If you dress the salad very lightly by tossing it with a small amount of oil-free dressing, the flavors of the vegetables really come through.

Variations:

- Red Salad: Red kale, radicchio, finely sliced red cabbage, French lentils, red onions, diced celery, beets, walnuts, raisins
- Arugula, onions, avocado, cucumbers, grape tomatoes, olives, garbanzo beans

Menu Palette #4: Entree-sized Salad
Red Salad Variation: Red cabbage, Radicchio, Beets, Red Onions and Raisins

Menu Palette #5: Bean Bowl with Vegetables and Grains. Sample Recipe: Garbanzo Beans, Tomatoes and Peppers with Brown Rice

Menu Palette #5
Bean Bowl with Vegetables and Grains

Low-fat, high-protein, and so tasty!

Legume Options
Black beans
Pinto beans
Garbanzo beans
Black-eyed peas
Lentils

Vegetable Options
Cauliflower
Cilantro
Corn
Eggplant
Fresh parsley
Fresh peppers
Garlic
Jicama
Leeks
Mushrooms
Olives
Onion
Potatoes
Shallots
Squash
Sweet potatoes
Tomatoes

Grain Options
Brown rice
White rice
Tortilla or flat bread

Liquid Options
Water
Vegetable broth

Spice Options
Cumin
Turmeric
Coriander
Curry powder
Basil
Oregano
Dill
Parsley
Paprika
Mint
Cayenne pepper
Chili powder
Onion powder
Garlic powder
Pepper

Condiments
Lemon juice
Lime juice
Vinegar
Dijon mustard
Salsa
Soy sauce
Tabasco
Sriracha

Extras
Avocado
Guacamole
Olives
Capers

Menu Palette #5: Bean Bowl with Vegetables and Grains

Sample Recipe: Garbanzo Beans, Tomatoes and Peppers with Brown Rice

Protein: 26.2 g
Carbohydrates: 90.4 g
Fat: 9.7 g
Fiber: 16.9 g

Target Index: 6.0
Calories: 489

Preparation Time: 30 minutes
Shortcuts: pre-cooked beans, pre-cooked rice

Menu Palette Option	Amount (US)	Amount (Metric)
Legume Option: Garbanzo beans	1 cup, cooked	170 g, cooked
Liquid option: Vegetable broth or water	1 cup, as needed	250 mL, as needed
Other vegetable option: Onions	3/4 cup, chopped	39 g, chopped
Other vegetable option: Garlic	1 small clove, diced or pressed	1 small clove, diced or pressed
Other vegetable option: Mushrooms	1/2 cup, sliced	113 g, sliced
Other vegetable option: Tomatoes	1/2 cup, diced	100 g, diced
Other vegetable option: Bell pepper	1/2 cup, diced	79 g, diced
Other vegetable option: Jalapeno pepper	1/4 Tablespoon, diced	1.5 g, diced
Spice option: Cumin	1 teaspoon	2.1 g

Menu Palette Option	Amount (US)	Amount (Metric)
Spice option: Paprika	1 teaspoon	2.1 g
Spice option: Coriander	1 teaspoon	1.7 g
Spice option: Dried parsley	1 teaspoon	0.5 g
Spice option: Dried mint (optional)	1/4 teaspoon	0.2 g
Spice option: Turmeric	1/4 teaspoon	0.6 g
Spice option: Cayenne pepper	1/4 teaspoon	0.5 g
Spice option: Black pepper	1/4 teaspoon	0.6 g
Seed option: Sesame seed	1 Tablespoon, ground or whole	2 g, ground or whole
Side dish option: Brown rice	1/2 cup, cooked	190 g
Condiment: Lemon juice	1 teaspoon	4.8 g

Preparation Tips

- Cook the beans ahead-of-time: Start with dried beans, and follow the usual cooking instructions: Sort and rinse them, then soak them overnight, or for several hours. To do a "quick soak," after sorting and rinsing the beans, bring them to a boil in a large pot with plenty of fresh water, then turn off the heat and let them soak for 2 hours. After soaking, rinse the beans well. Add salt (optional), a bay leaf or other seasonings and plenty of fresh water. Simmer on low heat until tender, about an hour, stirring occasionally and adding more water if needed.

- You can also cook the rice ahead-of-time: it takes brown rice about 40 minutes to cook, and other varieties about 20 minutes.
- If you're making brown rice, you might want to look up Dr. Barnard's recipe on YouTube; it's really good! Or just follow the usual cooking instructions for the variety of rice you're using.
- Slice all the vegetables, then heat a frying pan or wok on the stove.
- Brown the onions by stirring them in the hot, dry pan. Use a little bit of water or vegetable broth if needed, then lower the heat, and add the rest of the ingredients. Add more water or vegetable broth to keep everything moist.
- Vary the amount of spices to suit your taste.
- Serve with a lemon wedge. A squirt of fresh lemon juice makes this dish even more delicious!
- This recipe is reasonably low in fat and has no added oil. To reduce the fat content even more, don't add the sesame seeds.
- Try adding potatoes, cauliflower or eggplant to this recipe.
- This recipe's yield is an extra-large portion. If it's too much, save some for later.
- To make a hearty soup out of the beans and vegetables, puree them in the blender with more water or vegetable broth.

- Shortcut: Use a blender or food processor to make fresh, chunky salsa for bean bowl variations. Add the garlic and jalapeno first; chop them finely. Next add the cilantro, onions, lime juice and spices and blend a little more. Add the tomatoes last and blend just until the desired texture is achieved.

Variations:

- Black beans or pinto beans with fresh salsa and avocado served with a whole wheat tortilla, baked tortilla chips or an ear of fresh corn-on-the-cob
- Black-eyed peas with tomato, onion and pepper relish served with rice
- French lentils with red onion, capers and Dijon mustard served with rice
- Lima beans or navy beans seasoned with dill served with potatoes leeks and shallots

Understanding the Menu Palette Method

Why Menu Palettes? Why Not Recipes?

Conventional recipes are a great idea, especially for special occasions. I normally search online for a recipe when I want to prepare a specific dish and I even have a few plant-based cookbooks. For the purposes intended in this book, menu palettes can get you by day-to-day better than conventional recipes. With a little practice, a few basic menu palettes can support you in your health goals for most meals.

Drawbacks to Using Conventional Recipes

Recipes for the week may require too many different ingredients and may be too time-consuming: Some of the plant-based menu plans I've seen list meal after meal requiring its own unique list of ingredients, and a lot of preparation time. It's more feasible to just keep a standard slate of interchangeable, easy-to-prepare menu palette options on-hand.

There's something in the recipe that you don't like or someone is allergic to

Have you ever found a recipe that looked really good, until you read down to a certain ingredient that you or someone else either doesn't like or is allergic to? That happened to me once when I tried a new recipe to make a special dish for a potluck. There was one ingredient that just didn't sound good to me. I should have trusted my instincts.

What if someone you're cooking for won't eat a certain ingredient, (tofu, for example) but the recipe calls for it? It can be difficult to know whether to try to substitute another ingredient, just leave it out, or find a different recipe altogether. Within the menu palette structure, options can be substituted freely, and improvised creations turn out amazing!

You're missing an ingredient

Have you ever set out to make a recipe, then realized that you're out of one of the ingredients? Or have you ever read through a recipe feeling excited and hopeful, then all of a sudden, there's an exotic ingredient that you don't already have, and aren't very excited about buying? Maybe it's an expensive spice that you might not even like or ever use again? Or maybe it's an unfamiliar fruit or vegetable that makes the whole recipe seem like too much trouble? With menu palettes, as long as you have the main ingredients, everything is fine.

You're missing a key piece of kitchen equipment

What can be even more frustrating than realizing you're missing an ingredient is to find that you're missing a kitchen appliance or cookware needed to make the chosen recipe. When that happens to me, I usually just give up on the recipe instead of wasting money on another piece of cookware that

I may rarely use. Too many unnecessary kitchen tools can create clutter. Fortunately, very few special kitchen items are needed for the menu palettes in this book, although a high-powered blender is a great thing to have.

You don't have enough time to make the recipe

Have you ever wanted to cook something from a recipe, but didn't because it would take more time than you had available? Sometimes multi-step recipes can take a lot of time. Conversely, "quick" recipes may use convenient canned or processed foods that are less healthy than fresh whole foods. The time to prepare menu palette meals can be scaled down by using fewer ingredients or less time-intensive ingredients.

Following recipes feels like too much of a chore

Sometimes it's too much trouble to get out the recipe book, measuring cups, measuring spoons, and pay careful attention to written instructions. I often prefer to design a meal in-the-moment, sparking my own creativity and trusting my own instincts. It's a lot more fun! And the results can be amazing!

Menu Palette Advantage: Aim for Your Targets!

A key advantage of using menu palettes instead of recipes is that it allows you to focus on the health-promoting foods we want to eat every day, and build solid recipes around those foods. Conventional recipes can be tailored, but using menu palettes is a simpler, more direct strategy to making the recommended nutritional targets an everyday habit.

Menu Palette Guidelines

In addition to the main ingredients, try to pick at least one option from each category. You can choose more than one option from any category if it sounds good, or none at all from any category. For example, you could make the Entree-sized Salad using more than one Green Leaf option. Or you could leave out the Other Vegetable option. Another example: In a pinch, the Grains with Fruit, Nuts and Seeds menu palette can be made with just plain oatmeal, although it's advantageous to include fruit, nuts or seeds to meet the daily targets.

The options marked as “Extras” are more calorie-dense, as are sweeteners, salad dressings with oil, dried fruits, nuts and seeds. Please be mindful if you’re calorie-conscious. Generally, there’s no need to measure, or count calories, but it’s a good idea to gauge your portion sizes with “Daily Dozen” recommendations in mind:

Daily Dozen Food	Serving Size	Daily Servings
Beans	1/2 cup	3
Berries	1/2 cup	1
Other Fruit	1 med sized whole, 1 cup fresh, or 1/4 cup dried	3
Cruciferous Vegetables	1/2 cup	1
Leafy Greens	1 cup	2
Other Vegetables	1/2 cup	2
Whole Grains	1/2 cup cooked cereal, 1 slice bread	3
Flaxseeds	1 T (ground)	1
Nuts	1/4 cup or 2 T nut butter	1
Spices	1/4 t Turmeric plus other spices	1

Menu Palette Logistics - How to Make it Work

Many people who try a plant-based diet go back to their old ways of eating because the plant-based diet was too restrictive and too difficult to execute. This section is the crux of menu palette logistics, a practical guide to staying on track, plate-by-plate, while enjoying flexibility and variety.

In order to *eat* the "Daily Dozen," you need to *have* the "Daily Dozen." Handling the logistical side of meal planning can make the difference between staying on track and what I will call "bailing out." Bailing out is when we fail to follow our own intentions for whatever reason, specifically "falling off-the-wagon" and eating animal-based foods like meat, fish, poultry or dairy because it was just easier. Bailing out can happen when it's too much trouble to prepare a healthy plant-based meal because of logistics—not having enough of the right foods on hand, not having time, not being at home, etc.

There are many reasons people “cheat,” on a plant-based diet, like peer pressure, social situations, cravings, feelings of deprivation, anxiety or boredom. I put “cheating” in quotes because there are moments when we don’t live up to our highest intentions, for whatever reason, but we’ve still made a choice in that moment; as individuals, we set our own priorities and make our own choices. Most of us don’t execute perfectly 100% of the time, and for me, there are degrees of “cheating.” For example, even using a convenient (but still plant-based) alternative is a bit of a cheat, like instant oatmeal or pre-cooked beans.

In my view, cheating is different from bailing out, but the two are related. For example, I would consider eating a fast-food hamburger “cheating,” but the question is why. If a person craved a hamburger and then ate one, then it’s “cheating.” If a person really wanted a healthy plant-based lunch, but was too busy and away from home, and the only food available was a hamburger, then it’s “bailing out.” It could be both! Logistical preparation can prevent “bailing out,” and being unprepared can lead to “cheating.”

For now, let's just focus on two logistical causes for bailing out:

- Not having enough time
- Not having enough of the foods needed on hand.

Learn to recognize when you're close to bailing out and try to make adjustments. Here are a few shortcuts to stay on track when it's not possible to prepare a proper meal:

- Having a smoothie instead of a salad because it's faster
- Making a drastically abbreviated version of a menu palette using minimally-processed foods
- Getting a ready-to-eat plant-based meal from a healthy grocery store instead of cooking
- Buying a plant-based meal from a vegan-friendly restaurant instead of cooking
- Eating a less nutritious but more convenient plant-based meal (like a microwaved potato or a vegan frozen dinner)
- Skipping a meal because there's not enough time to buy or prepare food

The worst-case is to get too stressed out, abandon your intentions and eat something that you'll regret later, or even derail your whole plant-based program. If you get off-track, don't worry; just get back on.

Selecting Groceries and Managing Supplies

There are apps, but I prefer to just use a scrap of paper and a pen to write my grocery list. Before I go shopping, I survey my refrigerator and my shelves to see what I need, and write my list. There is both art and science to every aspect of the menu palette method, including grocery shopping and inventory management. If you're just beginning to eat a plant-based diet and you need basic information, I'll offer some tips. Many people reading this book may be long-time successful plant-based eaters, and I'm sure that many people reading this book know more about cooking than I do. I'm not a chef at all; I'm only sharing things that have worked well for me, in hopes that they might be helpful to others.

Grocery Shopping Tips

The "Countdown" from Freshness

Part of the logistical struggle of creating fresh healthy meals day after day is making sure there are enough menu palette options on-hand to meet the recommended daily requirements and to create appealing, satisfying meals. Fresh vegetables and fruits are very healthy and naturally appealing. Their bright colors cue our senses that they are good to eat. Unfortunately, we only have a certain window of time to use produce before it's no longer good-to-eat; the "countdown" starts the moment we put the produce item in our cart. Often, as produce goes bad, its bright colors fade, or it takes on a bad smell. Fresh greens can go bad pretty quickly, sometimes within three or four days.

I encourage you to find out the best ways to prolong the freshness of the vegetables and fruits you enjoy. Many vegetables and fruits are best kept in the refrigerator bins, while others are best kept unrefrigerated. Some vegetables and fruits freeze well, while others do not. I will leave it to you to decide how to maintain your fresh produce in the ways that suit you best. Check online and on YouTube for information. Many people use environmentally-conscious household products, excluding things like plastic bags and paper towels. I'm still learning and evolving in this area.

Tip 1: Develop a Cadence for Produce Shopping that Supports Your Needs

Satisfying the daily per-person recommended amounts of daily greens, other vegetables, berries and other fruit can take some careful planning. Conversely, buying too much produce can cause waste; it's a delicate balance. Frozen vegetables and fruits are a good shortcut; some say they are as healthy as their fresh counterparts. Personally, I prefer to shop often so I always have fresh produce on hand. I grocery shop at least once a week, usually every three to four days, buying small amounts of needed items. Also, if you don't meet every requirement during the course of a day, just try to make it up on-average during the week, as best you can.

Tip 2: Stock the Needed Non-Perishable and Semi-Perishable Items

Grains, rice, and beans are easier to manage because they can be kept for months on a shelf. Dried spices and other seasonings, too, can be kept for months without spoiling. Nuts, seeds and dried fruit can be kept on a shelf, but may last better if refrigerated or frozen. Flaxseeds in particular can go bad quickly without refrigeration. Again, read labels and do research to find out the best ways to store the foods you like. Avoid keeping any type of food, spice or condiment too long, even non-perishables. Use it up, or throw it out.

Tip 3: How to Select Produce (unless you're ordering online)

I don't know about you, but I enjoy shopping for produce. I especially enjoy going to Farmers' Markets and my local organic grocery store. For most items, I know how to pick "a good one." How you select produce will affect your capability to succeed with menu palettes. It can be a matter of phasing the readiness of the menu palette components that you buy so they will be ripe and ready-to-eat at the right time. Many vegetables and fruits are ripe and ready-to-eat when bought, but others, bananas, kiwis, cantaloupes and avocados for example, may need a few days. If you need basic guidance on how to select produce, I encourage you to make an adventure out of it; ask people, look for YouTube videos and other sources. Have fun. It's a very worthwhile thing that you can enjoy all your life.

Look for produce in-season. Incorporate items that look irresistibly good into your menu palettes, even if they weren't on your grocery list. For example, if you had planned to buy a particular type of mushroom, but there's another type that looks fresher and more interesting, buy that one instead. This is a fun way to add more variety to meals. Conversely, if you were planning to use a particular menu palette option but it doesn't look very good, pick something else. For example, if you were thinking of buying a particular type of leafy green, like green kale, but what's available that day doesn't look very appetizing, then choose an alternative like arugula, if it looks fresher and more delicious.

Another important note: please feel free to substitute menu palette options freely. Just because a produce item isn't listed as part of the menu palette doesn't mean it can't be part of the "recipe." Menu palettes are just suggestions of compatible options, and are not intended to be exhaustive lists. Be creative! You can even create entirely new menu palettes of your own! As you're choosing menu palette options, the goal is to maximize the count of categories from Dr. Greger's "Daily Dozen," and Dr. Fuhrman's G-BOMBS to a sensible degree. Too many foods from too many categories might make a recipe inedible. Meals can be both delicious and healthy, so balance these objectives carefully.

Tip 4: Keep Some Convenience Items On-Hand, to Protect Against Bailing Out

Salads can be the hardest menu palette to plan for. In a pinch, you can use a few short-cuts such as pre-cooked garbanzo beans, pickled beets, and other specialty vegetables in cans, jars or bottles, although fresh ingredients are generally healthier. If you're short on kale, arugula, lettuce or spinach, you can use cabbage, which keeps for a longer time in the refrigerator's crisper bin. Red cabbage, sliced finely, is especially good, and very healthy.

Servings of oats can be prepared in advance, or quick oats can be a real timesaver. Also, keep at least a small supply of raw organic nuts and dried fruits on hand. They're great additions to both salads and breakfast grains, especially when you're low on fresh berries and other fresh items. A word of caution: generally there's an inverse relationship between a food's convenience and its healthfulness, so do your research, and be mindful. Occasionally, a less-healthy shortcut is okay, but try not to make it a habit.

Fresh beets and a more convenient alternative

Tip 5: It's Okay to be Flexible

Menu palettes can be enjoyed at any time of day, as either a meal or a snack. If you'd like to have oatmeal for dinner or as a snack, that's perfectly fine. Whatever helps you stay on track is okay.

Groceries and Supplies:

Plan which menu palettes you'll make and get what's needed from the lists of menu palette options. Here are some additional shopping tips.

Spices and Dried Herbs:

Here's a list of suggested spices and dried herbs to keep on-hand. Add your own favorites.

Basil
Bay Leaves
Black Pepper
Cayenne Pepper
Celery Seed
Chili Powder
Coriander
Cumin
Curry Powder
Dill
Five Spice Seasoning
Ginger
Ground Mustard Seed
Mint
Oregano
Parsley
Red Pepper Flakes
Salt (optional)
Turmeric

Condiments

Vinegar (various varieties)
Nutritional yeast

Vinegar and nutritional yeast are generally viewed as healthy condiment options. You might want to restrict the use of soy sauce, mustard, ketchup, sriracha sauce, and salad dressings if they have too much salt, oil or sugar. Read labels carefully to make sure the condiments you use don't contain animal-based ingredients. For example, the brand of Worcestershire sauce that was a staple in my childhood home is made with anchovies.

Dr. Greger's Daily Dozen Food Categories Plus Dr. Fuhrman's "G-BOMBS"

Keep foods from each category on-hand. Be sure to have enough of each category to achieve the daily targets.

Beans
Berries
Other fruit
Cruciferous vegetables
Leafy greens
Other vegetables
Onions
Mushrooms
Whole grains
Flaxseeds
Nuts
Spices

Keeping Grocery Costs Down

If you're cost-conscious, here are a few tips:

Tip 1: If Not Organic, Then "Clean Fifteen"

Organic produce and foods are generally more expensive than conventional. If you either can't afford to or choose not to spend the extra money on organic produce, buy conventional. The priority is to eat fresh vegetables and fruits daily. Check the Environmental Working Group's "Dirty Dozen" and "Clean Fifteen" to see which conventional produce is recommended. The specific vegetables and fruits on the Environmental Working Group's "Dirty Dozen" and "Clean Fifteen" are not static; the list is researched each year. You can find the current lists on the EWG website (www.ewg.org).

Tip 2: Eat Berries and Leafy Greens First

Try not to waste food. If you find you're throwing away too much of your pricey organic produce, eat the foods that spoil the fastest first. Generally, berries and leafy greens spoil quickly, while citrus fruits and root vegetables can last much longer. Try to prioritize the fresh items with the shortest "countdown." Also, consider shopping more frequently and buying less each time, more of a "just-in-time" approach. Consider "phasing" your produce as best you can. For example, leafy greens are a key "Daily Dozen" item that can go bad very quickly. Find ways to preserve the freshness of your leafy greens, but be prepared to shop for them more often. If shopping more often is difficult, try to find varieties that keep longer, or maybe even a frozen alternative.

Tip 3: "Stage" Your Produce When Possible

Also, when shopping for certain fruits and vegetables such as bananas, kiwis, or avocados, consider selecting the number needed per day at the appropriate level of ripeness. For example, choose ripe bananas for today and tomorrow, and green ones for a few days from now. As you're selecting an avocado, for example, you'll have a rough idea when it will be ready for your menu palette—today, tomorrow, etc. You'll be able to plan accordingly. If the produce you need is available in different stages of ripeness where you shop, "staging" produce in this way helps reduce waste.

Tip 4: Don't Overcommit

Another practical tip about grocery shopping, avoiding food waste and staying on track: be realistic. As you place your produce items in your grocery cart, consider the amount of preparation time that will be required, and whether or not it's feasible for you within the "countdown" period. For example, sometimes I will bypass a labor-intensive produce item if I know I have a particularly busy work-week or out-of-town travel. If I know I won't have the time needed to prepare it; it's best to wait for an easier week. I might choose more convenient options including pre-washed salad greens, or whatever I need to support my success. Know your limits, and have compassion for yourself. Be flexible, stay in the moment. Give yourself any advantage you need.

Tip 5: Cook or Freeze What You Can't Finish

If you're not able to eat all the fresh produce you've bought before it goes bad, try to cook it or freeze it. Frozen bananas are great for smoothies. If you cook carrots, they will last for a few more days, or you can freeze the cooked carrots. If spinach isn't fresh enough to be enjoyed raw, it might be tolerable if in a smoothie or if cooked. Not every fruit or vegetable is suitable for cooking or freezing; check online or on YouTube if you're not sure.

Tip 6: Keep Menu Palette Options Simple

Maintaining a plant-based diet can be expensive, but it doesn't have to be. You can keep costs down by basing your menu palettes on less expensive items. Vegetables and fruits in-season tend to be less expensive. Buying vegetables and fruits in their whole form (not in convenient packaging) is usually less expensive. Frozen vegetables and fruits can also be a good buy. If buying a vast array of fresh vegetables and fruits for the Entre-sized Salad menu palette is too expensive, then just stick to a few low-priced options. Staple foods like oatmeal, beans, lentils and brown rice are very nutritious and can be very reasonably priced. Buying grains, legumes, nuts and seeds in bulk can be more economical, depending on where you shop.

Menu Palette #4: Entree-sized Salad
Green Leaf Salad Variation: Baby Arugula, Sliced Red Cabbage, Cucumbers, Red Onions, Watermelon Radish, Blueberries and Garbanzo Beans

How to Stay On track: Learning to Love Your Plant-Based Diet

People may have a hard time sticking with a plant-based diet for many reasons. This section is geared to those who are interested in making a plant-based diet a way of life, but struggle to stay on track.

Define Success: Be Intentional

If you're just getting started on your plant-based journey, it's a good time to reflect on your values and desires, think about your priorities and set your objectives. Be fully intentional; write things down.

Set Your Priorities, Set Objectives

Set an attainable standard for success that is appropriate and real for you. Be realistic. Set yourself up for success, not failure. It may be easiest to start small, then build on your successes over time. There is almost always more room for growth as we evolve and live according to our values and intentions.

Try not to set yourself up for failure by making your goals overly strict. For example, instead of: "I'll never eat another bite of any animal-based food for the rest of my life," maybe, "just for today, I will make healthier food choices, excluding animal products, and eating more vegetables and fruits." If being plant-based for the rest of your life feels too overwhelming or depressing, then just do it for one day, every day, for the rest of your life. I remember when I ran my first 10-mile race. I asked my coach, "Do you really think I can run ten miles?" He said, "No. I think you can run one mile ten times." And I did. An old saying that I find useful in trying times is "my short-term goal is noon; my long-term goal is midnight." Sometimes a day, a week, a month, or the holiday season can seem unmanageable. If we steer clear of bad influences, and focus on our "why" power day-by-day, we can get by.

Why-Power: Reasons People Switch to a Plant-Based Diet

Prevent or Reverse Disease

Eliminating animal products and eating a low-fat diet rich in fresh vegetables and fruits may eliminate risk factors entirely for many common chronic diseases including heart disease, cancer, diabetes, high blood pressure.

Maintain a Healthy Weight

Eating more fresh vegetables and fruits and eliminating processed foods contributes to maintaining an appropriate Body Mass Index. Carrying extra weight is a risk factor for many common chronic diseases.

Example of a Value-based goal: Health related and weight related

> "Just for today, I choose to honor my body with high-quality foods, reducing my risk of disease,

enabling me to live more fully and to better serve those who depend on me."

Improve Athletic Performance and Recover Faster

Since the documentary "The Game Changers" was released, interest in plant-based diets has increased as a means of enhancing athletic performance and reducing downtime between workouts, especially as we get older. Many famous elite athletes tout the benefits of following a plant-based regimen.

Example of a Value-based goal: Athletic Performance related

"Just for today, I strive to be the strongest version of myself that I can be. I fuel my body with everything it needs for peak performance while eliminating detrimental foods."

Decrease Your Carbon Footprint

Many people are casually, passively contributing to the destruction of planet earth through menu choices. By eating a plant-based diet, we can reduce our support of industries that are major contributors to the world's greenhouse gases.

Example of a Value-based goal: Environment related

> "Just for today, I choose to reduce my support of industries that are the most detrimental to the future of our planet."

Denounce Animal Cruelty

I began my plant-based journey for health reasons, but in time, my ethics evolved. Although I'd eaten meat, fish, poultry, dairy and eggs all my life, after I'd stopped for a while, I had the objectivity to realize that I had been complicit in the systematic cruelty that occurs. I encourage others to consider withholding their financial support from these industries that increase the quotient of cruelty in our world every day. I mean dairy, too. Dairy farming is the long-con because many dairy cows are also eventually slaughtered for their meat after years of abuse.

Example of a Value-based goal: Animal rights related

> "Just for today, I choose to withdraw my support of cruel animal farming practices to promote a more peaceful world for all living creatures. I will consider the consequences of choices I once made so casually."

Now it's your turn

Right now, jot down your top reason why you would switch to eating a plant-based diet. It does not have to be one of the examples listed; make it your own. If you can't pick just one, more than one is okay. This is your "why" power. Why power will keep you on track even when your will power wanes.

Transitioning to a Plant-Based Diet

If you haven't stopped eating animal products yet, do what you have to do to make the change. Maybe you'll want to start slowly, one day a week, then add extra days one at a time. Or maybe you'll want to start by eliminating one type of food at a time, for example, eggs, dairy, meat, poultry, and seafood, until there are no more animal-based foods in your diet. If you want the health benefits, it's best to go all the way, no half-measures. It's also very important to eat a well-balanced array of healthy foods each day, low in fat, high in fiber.

While transitioning, it's possible to cook meals as you normally would, but use plant-based substitutes for meat, fish, eggs, and dairy. For example, if you would normally make baked chicken with mashed potatoes and a vegetable side-dish plus a salad, you can leave out any animal-based ingredients that you might normally add to the salad (bacon bits, cheese, dressings made with buttermilk or mayonnaise, or croutons if they're made with any type of dairy) or use plant-based substitutes. For the mashed potatoes, you could make them using plant-based substitutes for the milk and butter. Prepare the vegetable side-dish with no butter, cheese, or broth.

Using substitutes can be a great way to stay off meat and cheese as you transition, but "vegan" processed foods may have a lot of salt, fat, or other unhealthy additives. Finding palatable vegan alternatives while transitioning can mean the difference between success and failure. That being said, work towards eating more and more plant-based foods in their whole form, avoiding processed foods even if they're marked "vegan."

Adjusting to Living Plant-Based

Give Your System a Chance to Adapt

Before you know it, after switching to a plant-based diet, you may find yourself enjoying meals even more than you did as an omnivore. The colors and flavors of fresh vegetables and fruits come alive when they are eaten in their natural form. You may find yourself looking forward to your Green Citrus Smoothie, or Green Leaf Entrée Salad with an unexpected feeling of intense anticipation! With a little time, effort and patience, we can grow to love the foods that love us back! Here are some tips.

Dealing with Cravings

Many of us are accustomed to salty, greasy, and sugary processed foods. There can be an addictive quality. If you stay on track, in time, food cravings will pass. When the "flash" of a food craving arises, try to focus on your "why" power and let it pass without acting on it.

Drs. Douglas J. Lisle and Alan Goldhamer put forth some ideas in their book The Pleasure Trap that I found useful in understanding food cravings. Our brains are wired to seek satisfaction and minimize effort, so we may be naturally drawn to calorie-dense foods. I used to feel guilty for my seeming lack of self-control and poor judgement. Why did I prefer high-calorie processed foods to healthier foods like fresh fruits and vegetables?

To help myself be more successful in sticking to my conscious choices, I put calorie-dense foods out-of-sight. For example, if I have a container of nuts, I put it in the cupboard or the refrigerator, not on the countertop. It's too easy to impulsively eat a handful or two while my oatmeal is cooking. It's also necessary to break the addiction to salt, oil and sugar by abstaining, or even by cutting way back. Staying on track while your tastes change is highly beneficial. After a while, many people find that the processed foods we used to eat are way too sweet, greasy or salty to be enjoyable anymore.

Not Liking the New Foods

Except for when there is an allergy or other medical reason not to, it is generally advantageous to eat foods that are part of the “Daily Dozen,” “G-BOMBS” and “Power Plate.” In Dr. Greger’s “Daily Dozen,” important food categories are: beans, berries, other fruit (other than berries), cruciferous vegetables, leafy greens, other vegetables (other than cruciferous vegetables and leafy greens), whole grains, flaxseeds, nuts, and spices. A person doesn’t have to eat every food in every category, but eating a variety of foods from each category is health-promoting, particularly leafy greens and cruciferous vegetables.

If there are worthwhile foods in these categories that you just don't have a taste for, I recommend that you try them again and again, little-by-little, in different varieties, prepared in different (but health-promoting) ways. For example, cruciferous vegetables. Some cruciferous vegetable options are: arugula, bok choy, broccoli, Brussels sprouts, cabbage, cauliflower, kale, radish, and turnips. If you say, "I don't like any cruciferous vegetables," try different ones prepared in different ways. For example, if you say you don't like the taste of kale, try different varieties--maybe the taste and texture of baby kale would be easier to tolerate? Or if not kale, how about arugula? If you don't like boiled broccoli, have you tried eating it raw, or lightly steamed? Or have you ever tried roasted Brussels sprouts, or roasted cauliflower? Or salad with thinly-sliced fresh red cabbage?

Similarly, there are so many varieties of beans and lentils that even if you don't like kidney beans or green lentils, it's still possible to find a go-to option. If you haven't already begun a daily bean habit, I'd like to encourage you. It's probably one of the simplest things a person can do to improve health from the inside-out and increase longevity. Just try to find at least one go-to option in each "Daily Dozen" and "G-BOMBS" category. Then, from time-to-time, keep giving other health-promoting foods you didn't like before another try. It's surprising how tastes can change over time.

Digestive Distress

After you've switched to a plant-based whole food diet as described, you may find that your digestive system needs time to adapt, especially if you're eating more vegetables, fruits, beans and lentils than you're used to. For me, the biggest change was eating a lot more beans than I ever had before. It took my system several months to adjust. If you have that problem too, here are the tips that I found most helpful:

Instead of Buying Pre-Cooked Beans, Cook Dry Beans at Home

Consider starting with dry beans and lentils at home instead of packaged pre-cooked beans (usually in a can or a box). Wash, soak, drain, rinse, boil until soft, and rinse again; more rinsing can help a lot with digestibility. I even heard that adding a bay leaf or a pinch of baking soda would help. Cooking the beans longer, until they're very soft, may make them easier to digest. Some people recommend using an instapot or pressure cooker to cook beans faster, or letting them simmer all day in a crock pot. These methods may work well for you, too. Personally, I just keep small pots of beans and lentils soaking or cooking on the stove most days, like a rotation. I like the variety of small batches and there's little waste, but making larger batches and freezing a few servings for convenience would also be a great idea.

Start Slowly

Try eating just a tablespoon of beans or lentils at first, then build up slowly, day-after-day to a full serving.

Consider trying different types of beans and lentils. Even after carefully cooking beans at home, some varieties may be harder to digest than others; this can vary from person to person. My go-to legumes are garbanzo beans (also known as chickpeas) and French lentils. They are delicious and their flavor is perfect for the Green Leaf Entrée Salad Menu Palette. I also enjoy many other varieties of legumes, including black beans that are very high in iron and black-eyed peas. Some sources say black-eyed peas are the easiest to digest. As you experiment, keep in mind which beans were the easiest for your system to digest, and make those your go-to varieties for daily use.

Strategies for Hard Situations

There will be times where it's difficult to stay on track. Planning for these times will help, but will not solve every problem. You can plan strategies in advance—how you prefer to handle particular situations, even if it means a momentary compromise. For example, if a favorite relative has gone to a lot of trouble to make your favorite dessert, not realizing that you've changed your diet, instead of a whole serving, maybe take only a taste to say how delicious it is, and to express appreciation. But be careful; sometimes even a taste can lead to cravings. Generally, it's easier to just stay on track; it gives a consistent message to those around you as well.

Holiday Gatherings and Parties

Suggestion: Bring a plant-based dish to holiday gatherings, parties, and events.

If you can't bring a dish, eat a healthy plant-based meal before you go.

Work-Related Events

Suggestion: Eat before you go or bring your food if practical. If not, try to make arrangements in advance if food is served, to see if there will be "vegan" options.

Travel

When staying in a hotel, try to get a room with a kitchen if possible. Most hotels can provide at least a small refrigerator. Stock the refrigerator with enough healthy foods such as vegetables, hummus, and fruits, to last the duration of the trip. Instant oatmeal is an easy breakfast option if boiling water is available. There are good online resources to find plant-based restaurants while traveling, but be careful; sometimes sources confuse vegetarian and vegan.

"Vegetarian" may include dairy, eggs, or even seafood. Use the word "vegan" to qualify restaurants and menu options. The word "vegan" may imply certain ethical and philosophical positions that you may or may not agree with, but in general, the word "vegan" is well-understood to mean no meat, poultry, seafood, dairy, eggs, or other animal products, such as chicken stock or oyster paste.

Eating in Restaurants with Friends or Family

Many restaurants offer vegan options, or will allow substitutions or omissions. When making plans to eat out, if you can, suggest a restaurant that has good plant-based options. If you aren't able to choose the restaurant, check the menu in advance to see what's available. You can even call the restaurant in advance if there don't seem to be any good options. Worst case: eat at home in advance, and just have a side salad or something small while you enjoy the company of your friends and family.

Meals at Home with Meat-Eaters

When you have to prepare meals suitable for meat-eaters, consider making "modular" meals where meat can be added separately. For example, pasta with marinara sauce, with the meat cooked separately. Or "make your own tacos," where there are plenty of plant-based ingredients (black beans or pinto beans, salsa, and avocados), with meat and cheese to be added separately by those who want it.

Dealing with Information, Misinformation, Conflicting Information and Doubt

Misinformation about fitness, weight loss and nutrition in general is very common. Years ago, a fitness coach at my gym told me that if I exercised, what I ate didn't really matter. I couldn't disagree more. As an athlete, I want to nourish my system with healthy, nutritious foods that will enhance my performance and recovery. In terms of weight loss, what we do at the table matters far more than what we do at the gym. A person eating the standard American diet consumes a lot of empty calories. On average, a person running on a treadmill for 20 minutes burns about 300 calories, but a fast-food meal can easily be about 1,100 calories.

It's hard to compensate for high-calorie eating with exercise; the math just doesn't work. For many of us with sedentary jobs, the number of calories we burn each day doesn't match up to the high-calorie bill-of-fare that the standard American diet includes. Even if we exercise several times a week, it's hard to maintain a healthy weight without managing what goes on our plate.

People also seem to be preoccupied with getting enough protein. Protein shakes have been popular for years, but is it healthy to overload the body with so much protein, especially in such unnatural forms? Many people are against carbs, although a lot of the very healthiest foods that are most protective against chronic disease, vegetables and fruits, are high in carbs, and our brains run on carbs! Some people are even concerned about not getting enough of the "good fats," even though a healthy diet of vegetables, fruits, legumes, grains, nuts and seeds has more than enough fat, even without added oils.

I blame the powerful interests for propagating misinformation to sell us food, supplements and nutritional information that works to our detriment so that they can get richer. To deal with the flood of misinformation, I have changed my thinking about nutrition in the following ways: When I first hear a claim about health, fitness and nutrition, I treat it with skepticism. I believe nothing until I've had a chance to look for research and information through reputable sources. I trust (but verify, as best I can) information coming from a cadre of knowledgeable plant-based resources. There is so much information out there that it can be hard to know where to turn for the straight truth about proper nutrition. Even our own doctors can give us bad advice, because in medical school the topic of nutrition isn't generally emphasized. Many medical doctors are just that—doctors of medicine, meaning they just prescribe medicine and perform medical procedures. Many treat chronic illnesses with medication, never really healing their patients.

I have chosen to trust the well-meaning doctors who lead the plant-based movement—they continue to inspire people like me with their wisdom and encouragement (please see the References section). I choose to rely on certain experts in order to manage my feelings of doubt. Often, when the food or pharmaceutical industry want the masses to act against their own best interest, they point to contradictory studies. When there's doubt, many people will just throw up their hands and do whatever is easiest. I think it's only natural to wonder, and to have feelings of doubt when faced with conflicting information, but doubt can derail you; don't let it.

A Few Words About Weight Control

Like most people, I've known many people who want to lose weight or keep from gaining weight. From a health perspective, a good metric to determine whether a person's weight is in a healthy range is Body Mass Index (BMI), a calculation using a person's height and weight. The resulting value is compared to a range of values categorized Underweight, Healthy, Overweight, or Obese. (If you want to check your BMI, search for a BMI calculator online.) My body mass index used to be too high, putting me at risk for chronic diseases. Now, it's well within the healthy range. I've heard that statistically, among omnivores, vegetarians and vegans, vegans are the only group whose average BMI is in the healthy range. In time, overweight people eating a low-fat, high-fiber plant-based diet rich in fresh vegetables and fruits can achieve a healthy BMI. Managing calorie density can help.

Calorie Density

I don't know where the topic of calorie density originated; I've heard of it many times, from many sources. It may have originated with Jeff Novick, who is associated with the McDougall Center and Forks Over Knives. I agree with the experts who recommend managing calorie density. If you're trying to control your weight, taking calorie density into consideration when choosing menu palette options makes sense and can be very helpful.

There are three primary macronutrient categories present in food (and therefore every menu palette option): protein, carbohydrate, and fat. While most foods are higher in one of the three macronutrient categories than the other two, most foods have some measure of all three. For example, oatmeal is a grain—a starchy food that is high in carbohydrates. But nutritionally, it has all three macronutrients. In 100 grams of raw oats, there are about 389 calories, 16.9 grams of protein, 66.3 grams of carbohydrate, and 6.9 grams of fat. Gram-for-gram, protein and carbohydrates each have four calories, but fat has nine. The corresponding calorie counts by macronutrient are 67.6 calories of protein, 265.2 calories of carbohydrates and 62.1 calories of fat. (Note: The calorie counts of the macronutrients don't add up to the overall stated calories due to other nutrient values and rounding.)

Fat is more than twice as calorie-dense as the other two macronutrients. So, gram-for-gram, theoretically, if a person eats foods that are lower in fat, they will consume fewer calories by the time their stomach feels full.

The Calorie Density Scale
(from the Forks Over Knives website)

Foods	Calories per Pound Range
Vegetables	60 - 195
Fruit	140 - 420
Potatoes, Pasta, Rice, Barley, Yams, Corn, Hot Cereals, Beans, Peas, Lentils	320 - 630
Breads, Bagels, Fat-free Muffins, Dried Fruit	920 - 1,360
Sugars (i.e., sugar, honey, molasses, agave, corn syrup, maple syrup)	1,200 - 1,800
Dry Cereals, Baked Chips, Fat-free Crackers, Pretzels, Popcorn	1,480 - 1,760
Nuts/Seeds	2,400 - 3,200
Oils	4,000

Key Observations about the Calorie Density Scale

- Oil is the most calorie-dense thing you can eat. Pound-for-pound, oils and fats add more calories to our diet than any other macronutrient. The most efficient way to reduce calories is to reduce fat; a shortcut is to eliminate added oils, bearing in mind that there is still a good measure of fat in the rest of the foods we eat.
- The second most calorie-dense category is nuts and seeds. Most experts agree that certain nuts and seeds are high in important nutrients and small portions should be part of a healthy diet.
- Tip: If you have the option, it's healthier to cook with (or eat) the whole-food source of the oil instead of the oil. Oil is a highly processed food. It has no fiber, and is 100% fat. Even unsaturated fat may be a factor in certain health conditions, as well as obesity. Eating olives, coconut, sesame seeds, etc., in their whole form may be healthier than eating the oil produced from them because at least there is some fiber, and the whole-food counterpart is less processed.
- Not only are vegetables and fruits the least calorie-dense, they are also among the most health-promoting and high in vitamins, fiber, and minerals.
- There is a big jump in calorie density as soon as we get beyond the core recommended foods. Dried fruit is more desirable than the other items in its category because smaller amounts are usually consumed. It still has a high nutritional value, although the fresh fruit alternative would be a healthier choice.

- Most sugars are empty calories (offering no redeeming nutritional benefit), but molasses has iron, calcium, and potassium. I sometimes opt for molasses instead of other sweeteners for that reason, although its flavor is too strong for most uses.
- Processed foods should be avoided, especially for people who are limiting calories.

Menu Palettes and Calorie Density

The calorie content of meals prepared using menu palettes can be scaled up or down by adding or reducing the amount of calorie-dense options, and by adjusting the overall portion size. The most effective way to reduce the calorie content of a meal is to eliminate calorie-dense options, particularly those high in fat such as nuts, avocados, and salad dressings with oil. Next, cut back on grains, then legumes until the body mass index is in the normal range. It might happen quickly (within a few months), but if it takes longer, stay on track and be patient. If you feel like you're not losing weight fast enough, try keeping a food diary for several days using an app like My Fitness Pal to identify any sources of hidden calories that might be undermining your efforts. Conversely, for people who have trouble keeping weight on, it's easy to add calorie-dense options to menu palette meals at will.

A Few Words About Beverages, Alcohol and Caffeine

The most health-promoting beverage is fresh, clean water. Instead of commercially-produced beverages, choose water.

Generally speaking, drinking alcoholic beverages does not enhance human health, and there are more risk factors than most people know. Red wine has been touted as a key to long life. In his book The Blue Zones, Dan Buettner reported that some of the world's longest-living people drank locally-produced red wine daily, but it can't be said for sure whether drinking commercially-produced red wine each day would have the same effect for the rest of us. Scientific studies have shown that alcohol use can be risky even in amounts as small as one serving per day. I'd like to encourage readers who drink alcohol to seek out research from trustworthy sources, then consider eliminating or reducing their alcohol intake as appropriate.

Drinks high in caffeine such as coffee or tea may also have harmful effects for some people. Coffee has pros and cons, but is generally thought not to be so bad, especially for people who drink three cups a day or less. Green tea is generally thought to be health promoting, as every reader has probably heard.

A Brief Word about Supplements: Vitamin B12

Many doctors say that it is necessary for people on a plant-based diet to take a vitamin B12 supplement because without animal-based foods, we would most likely not get enough. Not getting enough vitamin B12 can cause health problems such as anemia or nerve damage. A person could become very sick or even die. Fortunately, it's very easy to shore up vitamin B12 levels with supplements. As I am not a medical professional, I will not recommend dosage; please check a reputable online source like nutritionfacts.org for more information, or consult your doctor for testing and personalized dosage recommendations.

Conclusion: Living Plant-Based

Just as your tastes change as you adapt to a plant-based regimen, your social circle and activities may also change. I encourage you to continue taking steps to improve overall health—eliminate unhealthy habits, exercise regularly, avoid stress, get enough sleep, and make time to connect with the people you care about. If you want to make new friends who are also living plant-based, there are many great resources on social media. Changing my diet has changed my whole life for the better. I wish the same for you.

References and Resources

The following people and sources influenced and inspired the material in this book most of all. Look for their organizations, affiliations, books, podcasts, YouTube channels, YouTube interviews, websites, recipes, blogs, classes and documentaries; there are too many great contributions to list!

Doctors and Experts (alphabetic)

Dr. Neal Barnard
Dan Buettner
Chef AJ
Dr. T. Colin Campbell
Dr. Caldwell Esselstyn
Ann Esselstyn
Jean Esselstyn
Rip Esselstyn
Dr. Joel Fuhrman
Dr. Alan Goldhamer
Dr. Michael Greger
Dr. Michael Klaper
Dr. Anthony Lim
Dr. Douglas Lisle
Dr. James Loomis
Dr. John McDougall
Dr. Milton Mills
Dr. Dean Ornish
John Robbins
Ocean Robbins
Chris Wark
Dr. Kim Williams

Documentaries

Forks Over Knives

Cowspiracy

What the Health

The Game Changers

Eating You Alive

Fat, Sick and Nearly Dead, 1 and 2

YouTube Channels and Websites for Information and Recipes

Boho Beautiful

Environmental Working Group

Food Revolution Network

Forks Over Knives

Mic the Vegan

NutritionFacts.org

Physicians Committee for Responsible Medicine

Pick Up Limes

Plant Based News

Plant Strong

Made in the USA
Monee, IL
08 May 2023